FOREWORD

The agility and adaptability of the Royal Air Force has been crucial in meeting the challenges it has faced, and continues to face, in operations around the world. These operations have ranged from humanitarian relief in parts of North Africa and South East Asia to dealing with ongoing hostilities in support of coalition forces in Iraq and Afghanistan. With such a level of commitment it is no surprise that almost every operational aircraft the Royal Air Force has in service today is engaged in operations somewhere in the world.

The Royal Air Force, perhaps more than any other service, relies upon innovative technology to stay ahead of potential adversaries, and over the coming years there are a number of significant aircraft and equipment programmes due to be introduced. Cutting edge, high performance aircraft like the Typhoon F2 are now in squadron service and next-generation air-to-air and air-to-ground weapons are being introduced to provide a greater precision capability than previously seen. Further in the future the Royal Air Force will introduce the Lockheed Martin F35 Joint Combat Aircraft, which is a next-generation, multi-role, fighter aircraft. The F35 will place the Royal Air Force at the forefront of aviation technology and when coupled with the Typhoon F2 will keep the Royal Air Force at the leading edge of military aviation.

On the horizon are the state-of-the-art A400M tactical air transport aircraft and the Future Strategic Tanker Aircraft. When aligned alongside the existing C-130J and C-17 fleets these aircraft will significantly improve the Royal Air Force's strategic deployment capability. Support helicopters are also a major factor in the Royal Air Force's ability to deliver expeditionary air power anywhere in the world, and the recently introduced Merlin HC3 has [...] success in the support role in oper[...] is the first of a new generation of advanced, multi-role, medium support helicopters used in both the tactical and the strategic operational roles. Great advances are also being made in the world of airborne intelligence and command and control with the introduction of the Sentinel R1 and the forthcoming Nimrod MRA4. The Sentinel R1 is the most advanced long-range, airborne-surveillance system of its kind in the world and is unique to UK operations.

The introduction of UAVs will also change the way the RAF operates in a coalition environment. The Royal Air Force has been operating MQ1B Predator A UAVs in conjunction with the USAF and will shortly improve its capability with the introduction into service of the armed MQ9A Predator B. A 4-year project called Taranis is now underway to develop a UAV demonstrator which will lead to an unmanned combat aircraft that will enable judgments to be made on what UAVs can, or cannot provide, in operational theatres and hostile environments.

The introduction of these new aircraft will give the Royal Air Force a world beating capability in the prosecution and support of its agile, capable and adaptable expeditionary air force role. But, important as equipment is, it is only part of the story. The men and women who operate, maintain and support the equipment remain the Royal Air Force's most important asset. Their professionalism and commitment give the Royal Air Force its second-to-none battle-winning capability.

Defence PR (RAF) Publications

ROYAL AIR FORCE

AIRCRAFT OF THE RAF

AIRCRAFT 2

WEAPONS 88

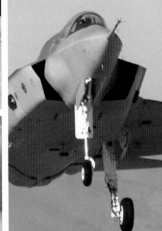

Expeditionary Air Wings (EAW)

No 121 EAW	Multi-role	RAF Coningsby
No 122 EAW	Ground Attack	RAF Cottesmore
No 125 EAW	Fighter	RAF Leuchars
No 135 EAW	Fighter	RAF Leeming
No 138 EAW	Ground Attack	RAF Marham
No 140 EAW	Ground Attack	RAF Lossiemouth
No 905 EAW	Multi-role	Falkland Islands

AIR COMBAT 1 GROUP

O **ROYAL AIR FORCE**

Squadrons   **No. 121 EAW**   3(F) Squadron   11(F) Sqaudron   17(R) Squadron   29(R) Squadron

> in the time it takes to read this sentence the
Typhoon can travel over 2 kilometres <

> TYPHOON F2

The Typhoon F2 provides the RAF with a highly capable and extremely agile multi-role combat aircraft, capable of being deployed in the full spectrum of air operations, including air policing, peace support and high-intensity conflict. Initial production aircraft will be deployed primarily as air-superiority fighters, but will quickly be equipped with a potent precision ground-attack capability. The pilot can carry out many functions by voice command or through a hands-on stick and throttle system. Combined with an advanced cockpit that is fully compatible with night-vision goggles, the pilot is superbly equipped for all aspects of air operations.

Powerplant
Two Eurojet EJ200 turbojets
Thrust: 20,000lb each

Dimensions
Length:	15.96m
Wingspan:	11.09m
Height:	5.29m
Weight:	21 tonnes
AAR:	Yes
Speed:	Mach 2
Ceiling:	65,000ft
Aircrew:	One

Weapon Systems
Planned to include
Missiles:	Storm Shadow, Brimstone, Meteor, AMRAAM, ASRAAM, ALARM
Bombs:	EPW II, Paveway IV
Gun:	Mauser 27mm

Sensors
Radar:	Captor ECR90, Pirate IR Search & Track
Targeting:	Litening III
Reconnaissance:	Litening III

Defensive Aids
Electronic counter measures
Laser warning receiver
Radar warning receiver
Towed radar decoy

ROYAL AIR FORCE

Squadrons No. 135 EAW 25(F) Squadron No. 125 EAW 43(F) Squadron 111(F) Squadron 56(R)Squadron

> using JTIDS the F3 can move to within 'kill' distance of a target before lighting up its own position-revealing radar at the very last moment <

TORNADO F3

The main visible difference from the Tornado GR4 is the longer fuselage, which permits greater internal fuel stowage. The pilot in the front seat flies and fights the aircraft, while the rear seat weapon systems officer controls the radar and defensive countermeasure systems. The aircraft is capable of operation in all weathers and at night, using night-vision goggles. In its usual air-defence role, the F3 can receive real-time information on approaching targets through a datalink from patrolling AEW E-3D Sentry aircraft and attack nominated targets using AMRAAM missiles. In the anti-radar role, F3s can pass information on the location of an opponent's radar site back to the Sentry or ground stations for onward relay to other aircraft or ground forces.

Powerplant
Two Turbo Union RB199 turbofans
Thrust: 16,410lb each

Dimensions
Length:	18.62m
Wingspan:	8.6m (extended 13.91m)
Height:	5.95m
Weight:	28 tonnes
AAR:	Yes
Speed:	Mach 2.2
Ceiling:	50,000ft+
Aircrew:	One pilot, one WSO

Weapon Systems
Missiles:	AMRAAM, ASRAAM, Skyflash, Aim-9L, ALARM
Bombs:	None
Gun:	Mauser 27mm

Sensors
Radar:	Foxhunter AI24
Targeting:	JTIDS
Reconnaissance:	None

Defensive Aids
Chaff and flare dispensers

ROYAL
AIR FORCE

Squadrons   **No. 138 EAW**   2(AC) Squadron   9(B) Squadron   13 Squadron   31 Squadron   41(R) Squadron

> TORNADO GR4

The Tornado GR4 is a variable geometry, two-seat, day or night, all-weather attack aircraft, capable of delivering a wide variety of weapons or of operating in the long-range, high-speed reconnaissance role. The aircraft can fly automatically at low level using terrain-following radar and by using its forward-looking infrared systems and night-vision goggles it is a very capable platform for night operations. The aircraft is currently being fitted with the RAPTOR pod, one of the most advanced reconnaissance sensors in the world, which makes it a world leader in the specialised field of all-weather, day and night tactical reconnaissance. Tornado GR4s are also being fitted with the Litening III laser targeting and reconnaissance pod, which can be used even when the aircraft is flying at maximum speed at low altitudes.

o. 140 EAW   12(B) Squadron   14 Squadron   617 Squadron   15(R) Squadron

the Tornado GR4 can fly supersonic at low level in total darkness without any input from the pilot

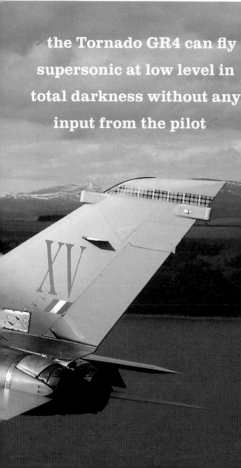

Powerplant
Two Turbo Union RB199 turbofans
Thrust: 16,000lb each

Dimensions
Length:	16.72m
Wingspan:	8.6m (extended 13.91m)
Height:	5.95m
Weight:	28 tonnes
AAR:	Yes
Speed:	Mach 1.3
Ceiling:	50,000ft
Aircrew:	One pilot, one WSO

Weapon Systems
Missiles:	Storm Shadow, Brimstone, ALARM, AIM-9L
Bombs:	Paveway II or III, EPW II or III, Paveway IV, BL755, General Purpose
Gun:	Mauser 27mm

Sensors
Radar:	Ground Mapping
Targeting:	TIALD, LRMTS Litening III
Reconnaissance:	RAPTOR, DJRP, Litening III

Defensive Aids
Skyshadow-2 ECM
Boz 107 chaff dispenser
Bol-IR decoy chaff dispenser

ROYAL AIR FORCE

Squadrons   **No. 121 EAW**   6 Squadron

> JAGUAR GR3A

The Jaguar is a ground-attack and reconnaissance aircraft, which has been upgraded over the years to maintain its potency. The most recent upgrade to GR3A standard included improved avionics, night-vision goggle compatible lighting, helmet-mounted sight, and new Head-up and Head-down Displays in the cockpit. These modifications have ensured that the Jaguar is fully capable for performing day and night operations. In the reconnaissance role, the Jaguar is fitted with an externally mounted pod and can also carry the TIALD pod for self-designation of targets or co-operative designation for attacks by other aircraft equipped with precision-guided weapons.

Powerplant
Two R-R Adour turbofans
Thrust: 8249lb each

Dimensions
Length: 16.83m
Wingspan: 8.69m
Height: 4.89m
Weight: 15.7 tonnes
AAR: Yes
Speed: Mach 1.4
Ceiling: 40,000ft
Aircrew: One

Weapon Systems
Missiles: AIM-9L
Bombs: Paveway II or III,
                     BL 755, General
                     Purpose
Rockets: CRV-7 Pods
Gun: Two 30mm Aden

Sensors
Radar: None
Targeting: LRMTS
Reconnaissance: DJRP

Defensive Aids
Radar warning receiver
Chaff and flare dispensers

> Jaguar was the first aircraft to be fitted with a 'star wars' helmet mounted missile sighting system <

ROYAL AIR FORCE

> the thrust from the Harrier's pegasus engine could support the weight of ten small cars <

> HARRIER GR7/GR7A

The Harrier GR7, which is operated under the organisational control of Joint Force Harrier, is used in the close-air-support role in direct support of ground troops attacking such targets as enemy troop positions, tanks and artillery. The first Harriers entered RAF service in 1969, making the RAF the first in the world to use its revolutionary vertical take-off and landing abilities, which allow the aircraft to fly in and out of areas close to the battlefield that would normally be off-limits to conventional aircraft such as the Tornado. The GR7/7A is being upgraded to the advanced GR9/9A standard.

Powerplant
R-R Pegasus 105 or 107 turbofan
Thrust: 21750lb (GR7)
                       23800lb (GR7A)

Dimensions
Length: 14.36m
Wingspan: 9.25m
Height: 3.55m
Weight: 14 tonnes
AAR: Yes
Speed: 574kts
Ceiling: 43,000ft
Aircrew: One

Weapon Systems
Missiles: AIM-9L, Maverick
Bombs: Paveway II or
                       III, EPW II or III,
                       BL 755, General
                       Purpose
Rockets: CRV-7 Pods
Gun: None

Sensors
Radar: None
Targeting: ARBS, TIALD
Reconnaissance: DJRP

Defensive Aids
ZEUS integrated EW suite

> HARRIER GR9/9A

The Harrier GR9 is a heavily updated development of the existing GR7, incorporating new communications and avionics systems giving it the ability to use a wide range of advanced precision weaponry. Integration and clearance of these upgrades will allow the RAF to hit a wider range of targets harder, at longer range and with less risk to aircrew. Alongside the GR9 upgrade programme, some aircraft are being fitted with more powerful engines to enable them to perform better in extremely hot climates, which degrade the performance of the existing Pegasus Mk105 turbofan. Aircraft with the improved engine will be designated GR9A.

Powerplant
R-R Pegasus 105 or 107 turbofan
Thrust: 21750lb (GR9)
                23800lb (GR9A)

Dimensions
Length: 14.36m
Wingspan: 9.25m
Height: 3.55m
Weight: 14 tonnes
AAR: Yes
Speed: 574kts
Ceiling: 43,000ft
Aircrew: One

Weapon Systems
Missiles: AIM-9L, Maverick
Bombs: Paveway II or III,
                EPW II or III,
                Paveway IV,
                Brimstone,
                General Purpose
Rockets: CRV-7 Pods
Gun: None

Sensors
Radar: None
Targeting: ARBS, TIALD
Reconnaissance: DJRP

Defensive Aids
ZEUS integrated EW suite

JOINT COMBAT AIRCRAFT

the JCA will be the first aircraft to display flight information directly on the pilot's visor instead of a HUD

The Lockheed Martin F35 Joint Strike Fighter will be known in UK service as the Joint Combat Aircraft (JCA) and is planned to replace the RAF and RN's Harriers. The UK version will be a multi-role fighter/attack aircraft designed to operate as a STOVL aircraft from land bases and from the next generation of aircraft carriers under study for the RN. The aircraft will offer several advantages over the Harrier: supersonic flight, improved survivability, internal and external weapons carriage, an increased range, stealth technology and easier supply and maintenance. Coupled with the Typhoon F2, the JCA will keep the RAF at the cutting edge of military aviation.

Powerplant

Pratt & Whitney F-135 turbofan

Thrust:	40,000lb

Dimensions

Length:	15.4m
Wingspan:	10.67m
Height:	4.6m
Weight:	22.7 tonnes
AAR:	Yes
Speed:	Mach 1.6
Ceiling:	50,000ft+
Aircrew:	One

Weapon Systems

Planned to include

Missiles:	AMRAAM, ASRAAM, Storm Shadow, Brimstone
Bombs:	Paveway IV
Gun:	Yes (dependant on mission)

Sensors

Planned to include

Radar:	APG-81 Grumman AESA Synthetic
Targeting:	Integrated into Mission System
Reconnaissance:	Internal or external pod

Defensive Aids

Planned to include
Full EW countermeasures system

Expeditionary Air Wings (EAW)

No 34 EAW	ISTAR	RAF Waddington
No 38 EAW	AT/ACSSU	RAF Lyneham
No 325 EAW	Maritime	RAF Kinloss
No 905 EAW	Multi-role	Falkland Islands

COMBAT SUPPORT 2 GROUP

ROYAL
AIR FORCE

the C-17 can land and take off on a runway the same length as 10 football pitches, that's less than one third the length of the runways at Heathrow and only 66 times the C-17's length

C-17A GLOBEMASTER III

C-17 Globemaster III is capable of rapid, strategic delivery of troops and all types of cargo to main operating bases anywhere in the world. The design of the aircraft also allows it to carry out high-angle, steep approaches at relatively slow speeds, thus allowing it to operate into small, austere airfields onto runways as short as 3500 feet long and only 90 feet wide. The C-17 can transport 45,360kgs of freight over 4500 nautical miles whilst flying at heights in excess of 30,000 feet. The C-17 gives the RAF a long range strategic heavy-lift transport aircraft that can operate close to a potential area of operations for combat, peacekeeping or humanitarian missions worldwide.

Powerplant
Four P&W F117- PW-100 turbofans
Thrust: 40,400lb each

Dimensions
Length:	53m
Wingspan:	52m
Height:	16.79m
Weight:	266 tonnes
Internal Fuel:	112.9 tonnes
AAR:	No
Speed:	550kts
Ceiling:	45,000ft
Range:	4700nmls
Aircrew:	Two pilots, one WSOp

Weapon Systems
None

Sensors
None

Defensive Aids
LAIRCM
Missile warning sensors
Flare dispensers (ALE-47)

> HERCULES C-130K C1/3

Hercules C-130K aircraft are used primarily to carry troops, passengers or freight and are capable of carrying up to 128 passengers, or 20 tonnes of palletised freight or vehicles, for up to 2000 nautical miles. In the aeromedical evacuation role either 64 or 82 stretchers can be carried, depending on the mark of aircraft and the stretcher configuration. The other main role of the C-130K is Transport Support (TS), which is the airborne delivery of personnel or stores by airdrop. The aircraft is particularly valuable in its TS role as it can be operated from unprepared and semi-prepared surfaces by day or by night.

Powerplant
Four Allison T56-A-15 turboprops
Thrust:	19,600lb
Propeller:	Hamilton hydromatic four-blade constant speed propeller

Dimensions
Length:	29.77m (CMk1) 34.89m (CMk3)
Wingspan:	40.38m
Height:	11.59m
Weight:	68.3 tonnes
Internal Fuel:	28.8 tonnes
AAR:	Yes
Speed:	310kts
Ceiling:	32,000ft
Range:	3000nmls
Aircrew:	Two pilots, 1 WSO, 1 flight engineer, 1 WSOp, 1 ground engineer

Weapon Systems
None

Sensors
None

Defensive Aids
DIRCM
Enhanced defensive-aids suite
(special task aircraft)

ROYAL
AIR FORCE

> # HERCULES C-130J C4/5

The RAF has a total of 25 C-130J air transport (AT) aircraft, which have been modified and upgraded to include new Allison AE turboprop engines and Dowty Aerospace six-bladed composite propellers. The new engines and advanced propellers, coupled with a new digital engine-control system, give the C-130J increased take-off thrust and better fuel efficiency than the C-130K; thus the external fuel tanks have been omitted. In addition to its AT role, the aircraft has been cleared for wider use in the tactical Transport Support (TS) role and is used for operational missions involving parachute operations and air despatch.

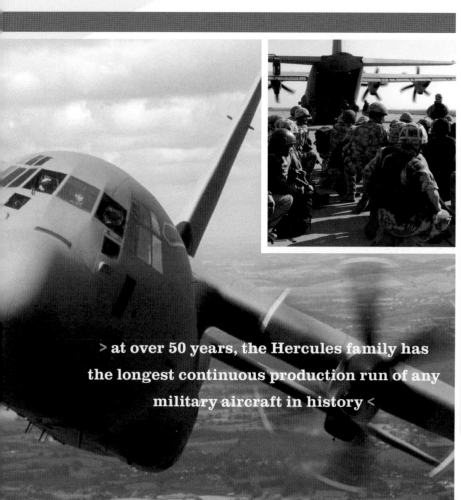

> at over 50 years, the Hercules family has the longest continuous production run of any military aircraft in history <

Powerplant
Four Allison AE 2100D3 turboprops
Thrust:	4700shp each
Propeller:	Dowty R391 six-blade variable pitch propeller

Dimensions
Length:	34.34m (CMk4)
	29.77m (CMk5)
Wingspan:	40.38m
Height:	11.65m
Weight:	33.9 tonnes
Internal Fuel:	20.8 tonnes
AAR:	Yes
Speed:	340kts
Ceiling:	35,000ft
Range:	3240nmls
Aircrew:	Two pilots, one WSOp

Weapon Systems
None

Sensors
None

Defensive Aids
Missile warning system (AAR-47)
Radar warning receiver (ALR-56M)
Chaff and flare dispensing system (ALE-47)

ROYAL AIR FORCE

> AIRBUS A400M

The A400M is being designed to bridge the gap between strategic and tactical operations provided by the C-17 and C-130 respectively. The aircraft has the nominal ability to carry a 25 tonne payload over 3000 nautical miles to remote civilian and military airfields. Troops (up to 116 paratroopers) and cargo can be dropped simultaneously either by parachute or gravity extraction, or by landing on short, unprepared or semi-prepared strips. The aircraft will be capable of operating either at low level (down to 150ft agl) or at high-level altitudes up to 40,000ft. The two-pilot flight-deck crew will have the benefit of state-of-the-art equipment, so greatly reducing crew workload.

Powerplant
Four EPI TP400 D6 turboprops
Thrust: 11,000shp each
Propeller: 8-blade variable pitch fully feathering

Dimensions
Length: 45.1m
Wingspan: 42.4m
Height: 14.7m
Weight: 137 tonnes
Internal Fuel: 38.31 tonnes
AAR: Yes
Speed: 510kts
Ceiling: 40,000ft
Range: 4100nmls+
Aircrew: Two pilots, 1 WSOp

Weapon Systems
None

Sensors
Radar: Type to be determined
Targeting: None
Reconnaissance: None

Defensive Aids (May include)
Radar warning receiver
Missile warning system
Chaff & flares dispenser
Directional Infra-red countermeasures
Towed radar decoy
Laser warning system
Missile approach warning system

> the A400M's engine power is equivalent to having 55 F1 cars strapped to its wings<

ROYAL AIR FORCE

E-3D SENTRY AEW1

E-3D Sentry aircraft are operated by the RAF in the airborne surveillance and command-and-control role. Whilst primarily procured as an airborne early warning aircraft, the E-3D has been extensively employed in the Airborne Warning and Control System (AWACS) role. The Sentry's roles include air and sea surveillance, airborne command and control, and weapons control. The aircraft's mission systems can separate, manage and display targets individually on situation displays within the aircraft, or it can transmit the information to ground-based and ship-based units using a wide variety of digital data links. The E-3D also operates as an extensive communications platform.

> **the Sentry can monitor a medium to high altitude area of over 820 times the size of Greater London** <

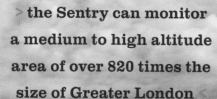

Powerplant
Four GE CFM 56 2A-3 turbofans
Thrust: 24,000lb each

Dimensions
Length: 46.68m
Wingspan: 44.98m
Height: 12.7m
Weight: 149.7 tonnes
Internal Fuel: 63.5 tonnes
AAR: Yes
Speed: 460kts
Ceiling: 35,000ft+
Range: 5000nmls
Aircrew: Two pilots, 1
                       WSO, 1 air
                       engineer, 10-man
                       mission crew,
                       3 engineers, 1
                       communications
                       operator.

Weapon Systems
None

Sensors
Radar: Northrop AN/APY-2
Targeting: None
Reconnaissance: Airborne and
                       surface targets

Defensive Aids
None

ROYAL AIR FORCE

> SENTINEL R1 ASTOR

The Sentinel R1 ASTOR (Airborne Stand-Off Radar) will provide a long-range, battlefield-intelligence, target-imaging and tracking radar for the RAF and the Army and will have surveillance applications in peacetime, wartime and in crisis operations. The aircraft will down-link radar information to a ground station which will receive, store and exploit the information and present it, via existing communications networks, in a variety of formats to commanders, tacticians and weapons operators on the battlefield. The Sentinel R1, which is due to enter service in December 2007, is the most advanced long-range, airborne-surveillance system of its kind in the world.

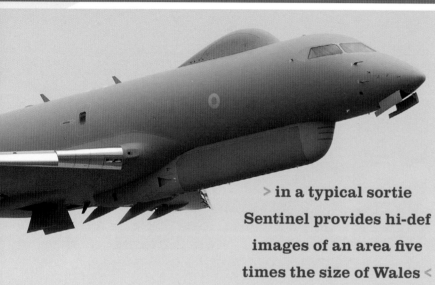

> in a typical sortie Sentinel provides hi-def images of an area five times the size of Wales <

Powerplant
Two R-R Deutschland BR710 turbofans
Thrust: 14750lb each

Dimensions
Length: 30.30m
Wingspan: 28.49m
Height: 8.23m
Weight: 45.15 tonnes
Internal Fuel: 19.75 tonnes
AAR: Yes
Speed: Mach 0.75+
Ceiling: 40,000ft+
Range: 5000nmls+
Aircrew: Two pilots, 3-man
                     mission crew

Weapon Systems
None

Sensors
Radar: Raytheon
                     ASARS-2

Defensive Aids
Missile warning system (AAR-57)
Radar warning receiver (ALR-56M)
Towed radar decoy (ALE-50)
Chaff and flare dispensers (Vicon 78)

Squadrons   No. 34 EAW   51 Squadron

> Nimrod R1 can scan and search over 11,000 radio frequencies every second <

NIMROD R1

The Nimrod R1 is a derivative of the Nimrod MR2 maritime patrol aircraft and has a highly sophisticated and sensitive suite of systems used for reconnaissance and the gathering of electronic intelligence. The ability of the Nimrod to transit at high speed and then loiter in an operational area at lower speed for long periods makes it ideally suited to the electronic intelligence gathering task. Air refuelling can extend the Nimrod R1's endurance should the task demand.

Powerplant

Four R-R Spey 251 turbofans
Thrust: 12,140lb each

Dimensions

Length:	35.86m
Wingspan:	35m
Height:	9.14m
Weight:	83.5 tonnes
Internal Fuel:	38.1 tonnes
AAR:	Yes
Speed:	360kts
Ceiling:	42,000ft
Range:	3800nmls
Aircrew:	Two pilots, 1 WSO, 1 air engineer, 25-man electronic reconnaissance crew

Weapon Systems
None

Sensors
None

Defensive Aids
None

ROYAL AIR FORCE

> the Nimrod can detect submarines by monitoring changes in the earth's magnetic field <

NIMROD MR2

MR2 Nimrod is the only jet-powered maritime patrol aircraft in military service and offers the advantages of speed and height in transit, while still capable of operating for long on-task periods. The Nimrod is used in four main roles: Anti-Submarine Warfare, Anti-Surface-Unit Warfare, Intelligence and Communications Support and Search and Rescue. Employment of the aircraft has evolved to take on an additional range of non-traditional tasks, including overland electro-optic IMINT (Image Intelligence) surveillance and communications support to coalition ground troops deployed in operational theatres.

Powerplant
Four R-R Spey 250 turbofans
Thrust: 12,500lb each

Dimensions
Length:	38.65m
Wingspan:	35m
Height:	9.14m
Weight:	83.6 tonnes
Internal Fuel:	38.2 tonnes
AAR:	Yes
Speed:	360kts
Ceiling:	44,000ft
Range:	3800nmls
Aircrew:	Two pilots, one air engineer, 9-man mission crew

Weapon Systems
Missiles:	Sting Ray torpedo, Harpoon
Bombs:	None
Gun:	None

Sensors
Radar:	Searchwater
Sonobuoys:	200+ active and passive
Targeting:	None
Reconnaissance:	Electro-Optic ImageIntelligence, ESM, MAD, Acoustic

Defensive Aids
Missile alert warning system
Chaff and flare dispensers

> NIMROD MRA4

Although the Nimrod MRA4 looks similar to the MR2, only the basic fuselage shell and the tail is shared between the two aircraft and the MRA4 will have completely new systems enabling it to fly for longer periods with a bigger payload in both weapons and sensors. The MRA4 will have a multi-tasking role, which will include its main roles of anti-submarine warfare, anti-surface unit warfare, maritime reconnaissance, search and rescue and ISTAR but, in addition, it will be used in law-enforcement tasks including anti-smuggling and anti-gun-running operations, fisheries protection and counter-terrorism duties. The MRA4 is expected to enter service around the turn of the decade.

Powerplant
Four RRD BR710 turbofans
Thrust: 14,900lb each

Dimensions
Length: 38.63m
Wingspan: 38.71m
Height: 9.29m
Weight: 105 tonnes
Internal Fuel: 38.2 tonnes
AAR: Yes
Speed: 520kts
Ceiling: 36,000ft
Range: 6000nmls+
Aircrew: Two pilots, 8-man mission crew

Weapon Systems
Missiles: Sting Ray torpedo
Bombs: None
Gun: None

Sensors
Radar: Thales 2000MR Searchwater
Sonobuoys: 180 active and passive
Targeting: None
Reconnaissance: Electro-Optic Image Intelligence, ESM, MAD, Acoustic

ROYAL
AIR FORCE

the total fuel carried by TriStar
would send a Ford Mondeo 61 times
around the world

> TRISTAR

The RAF has a mixed fleet of TriStars operating in the air transport (AT) and air-to-air refuelling (AAR) roles. The K1 and KC1 aircraft conduct AAR by using centreline hose-and-drogue units, whilst the C2 is used extensively for transporting up to 266 troops to world-wide destinations in support of exercises and operations. All versions of the TriStar aircraft can operate in the aeromedical evacuation role, including the option of installing a full stretcher fit if required for the repatriation of casualties.

Powerplant
Three R-R RB211-524B turbofans
Thrust: 50,000lb each

Dimensions
Length: 50.04m
Wingspan: 50.09m
Height: 16.87m
Weight: 245 tonnes
Internal Fuel: 96.9 tonnes (C2)
                      135 tonnes (K1/
                      KC1)
AAR: Yes (not as
                      receiver)
Speed: 520kts
Ceiling: 43,000ft
Range: 4500nmls
Aircrew: 4-9 dependant on
                      role or type

Weapon Systems
None

Sensors
None

Defensive Aids
LAIRCM (C2 & KC1)

ROYAL
AIR FORCE

| Squadrons | 101 Squadron | No. 905 EAW | 1312 Flight |

> VC10

The VC10 is a dual-role air transport (AT) and air-to-air refuelling (AAR) aircraft. In the AT role the aircraft is used for troop carrying, with accommodation for 124 passengers, or up to 20,400kgs of freight. The aircraft can also be used for aero-medical evacuation, for which up to 68 stretchers can be fitted. The bulk of the RAF's VC10 AAR fleet comprises VC10s of two different variants, the K3 and K4. Each aircraft is a three-point tanker, with fuel being dispensed from the two wing-hoses or from the single fuselage-mounted Hose Drum Unit. The aircraft is equipped with a modern flight-management system and the avionics required for full worldwide operations.

Powerplant
Four R-R Conway turbofans
Thrust: 20,000lb each

Dimensions
Length: 48.36m
Wingspan: 44.55m
Height: 12.04m
Weight: 154.4 tonnes
Internal Fuel: 69 tonnes (C1K)
                       82 tonnes (K3/K4)
AAR: Yes
Speed: 530kts
Ceiling: 43,000ft
Range: 5000nmls
Aircrew: Two pilots, one
                       WSO, one air
                       engineer

Weapon Systems
None

Sensors
None

Defensive Aids
Radar warning receiver
IRCM missile protection system

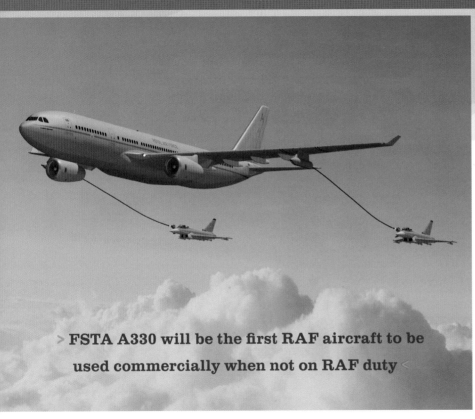

> FSTA A330 will be the first RAF aircraft to be used commercially when not on RAF duty <

FSTA A330

The Future Strategic Tanker Aircraft (FSTA) will replace the air-to-air refuelling capability and elements of the air transport work undertaken by the RAF's fleet of VC10 and TriStar aircraft. The RAF will continue to retain responsibility for all military tasks, whilst the contractor, Air Tanker Ltd, will own, manage and maintain the aircraft and also provide infrastructure and support, training facilities and some personnel. Air Tanker Ltd will operate the aircraft commercially when it is not required by the RAF. Current plans envisage FSTA progressively entering into service early in the next decade. The aircraft will be able to refuel from two wing-mounted pods and a centre-line fuselage unit. In its air transport role the aircraft will carry up to 330 passengers and 34 tonnes of freight.

Powerplant
Two R-R Trent 772B turbofans
Thrust: 71,100 lb each

Dimensions
Length: 58.82m
Wingspan: 60.3m
Height: 17.39m
Weight: 230 tonnes
Internal Fuel: 111 tonnes
AAR: Yes (not as receiver)
Speed: 475kts
Ceiling: 41,000ft
Range: 6400nmls
Aircrew: Two pilots, one Mission Systems Operator (AAR roles)

Weapon Systems
None

Sensors
Radar: Weather Radar
Targeting: None

Defensive Aids
LAIRCM

ROYAL AIR FORCE

> BAE 125 CC3

> the BAe 125 is the worlds most popular corporate jet, but it has also served with the RAF in Afghanistan and both Gulf wars <

The BAE 125 is operated by the RAF in the transport and communication roles. It is certified as a transport category aircraft and can operate in all weather conditions. The aircraft regularly provides a passenger service to the Royal Family, Government ministers and senior military officers. Its robust engineering, flexibility of operation and rapid turn-around times have made it a very successful aircraft, operated throughout the world in the VIP passenger role. In its communications role, the BAE 125 has provided support for most RAF peacekeeping and humanitarian operations worldwide, and currently operates between the UK and the Gulf region and on operations in both Afghanistan and Iraq.

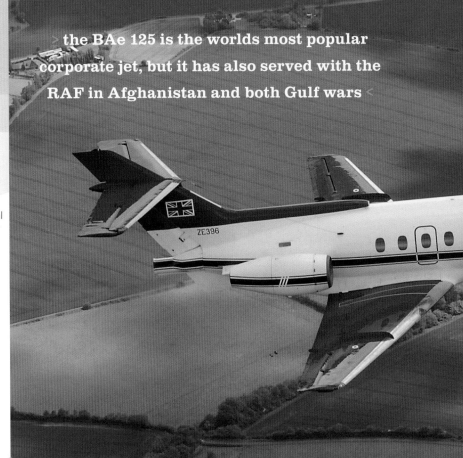

Powerplant
Two Garrett TFE731-3-1H turbofans
Thrust: 3700lb each

Dimensions
Length: 15.46m
Wingspan: 14.33m
Height: 5.49m
Weight: 11.6 tonnes
Internal Fuel: 9440lbs
AAR: No
Speed: 320kts
Ceiling: 41,000ft
Range: 1500nmls
Aircrew: Two pilots, one
                        cabin crew

Weapon Systems
None

Sensors
None

Defensive Aids
DIRCM

ROYAL
AIR FORCE

BAE 146 CC2

BAE 146 aircraft are operated by the RAF in the transport and communication roles. The aircraft has a trailing-axle main gear with a large damper unit, which allows the aircraft to operate from unprepared surfaces, including gravel and desert runways. The aircraft's excellent performance provides good short-field capability and allows it to operate from airfields located at up to 14,000ft above sea level. The BAE 146's excellent short-field performance, and its ability to operate from high or unprepared airfields in missile threat areas, mean that the aircraft is extremely versatile in support of overseas operations. The aircraft is extensively used in support of ongoing operations in Afghanistan and Iraq.

Powerplant
Four Avco Lycoming ALF502R-5
turbofans
Thrust: 6790lb each

Dimensions
Length: 26.18m
Wingspan: 26.8m
Height: 8.61m
Weight: 37 tonnes
Internal Fuel: 10.3 tonnes
AAR: No
Speed: 300kts
Ceiling: 30,000ft
Range: 1200nmls
Aircrew: Two pilots, two
                       cabin crew, one
                       ground engineer

Weapon Systems
None

Sensors
None

Defensive Aids
DIRCM

ROYAL
AIR FORCE

Expeditionary Air Wings (EAW)

No 903 EAW	Multi-role	Basrah
No 904 EAW	Multi-role	Kandahar
No 905 EAW	Multi-role	Falkland Islands

HELICOPTERS

ROYAL AIR FORCE

CHINOOK HC2/2A

Chinook aircraft are used primarily for trooping and for carrying internal and/or underslung loads and can carry up to 55 troops or 10 tonnes of freight. Secondary roles include search and rescue and casualty evacuation, in which role a total of 24 stretchers can be carried. The crew consists of either two pilots, or a pilot and a weapon systems officer and two air loadmasters. The Chinook is a very capable and versatile support helicopter that can be operated in many diverse environments ranging from cold weather arctic conditions to desert warfare operations.

Powerplant
Two Textron Lycoming T55-L712F turboshafts
Thrust: 3148shp each

Dimensions
Length:	30.18m
Rotor:	18.29m
Height:	5.78m
Weight:	11.3 tonnes
AAR:	No
Speed:	160kts
Ceiling:	15,000ft
Aircrew:	2 pilots (or one pilot, one WSO), 2 WSOps

Weapon Systems
Missiles:	None
Bombs:	None
Guns:	M134 Minigun, M60D machine gun

Sensors
None

Defensive Aids
Infrared Countermeasures System (ALQ-157)
Missile warning system (AAR-47 and ALQ-156)
Radar warning receiver (Sky Guardian)
Chaff and flare dispensers (Tracmor M130)

ROYAL AIR FORCE

>MERLIN HC3

The Merlin is the first of a new generation of advanced, medium support helicopters for the RAF. It is an all weather, day and night, multi-role helicopter used in both tactical and strategic operational roles. It is able to carry a diverse range of bulky cargo, either internally or under-slung or can carry up to 24 fully-equipped combat troops and, when required, will convert to carry 16 stretchers for casualty evacuation or during humanitarian and disaster relief operations.

Powerplant
Three R-R Turbomeca RTM 322 turbines
Thrust: 2263shp each

Dimensions
Length:	22.8m
Rotor:	18.6m
Height:	6.62m
Weight:	14.6 tonnes
AAR:	No
Speed:	167kts
Ceiling:	15,000ft
Aircrew:	2 pilots (or one pilot, one WSO), 2 WSOps

Weapon Systems
Missiles:	None
Bombs:	None
Guns:	Two 7.62mm GP machine guns

Sensors
Radar:	None
FLIR:	Turret Thermal Imaging
Targeting:	None
Reconnaissance:	None

Defensive Aids
Missile warning system (ALQ-54)
Laser warning system (AVR-2A (V))
Radar warning receiver (Skyguardian)
DIRCM (AAQ-24(V) Nemesis)
Chaff and flare dispensers

ROYAL
AIR FORCE

> PUMA HC1

Puma HC1s are used as battlefield helicopters within the Joint Helicopter Command and provide tactical troop and load movement by day or by night. The aircraft can carry 16 fully-equipped troops, or up to two tonnes of freight carried either internally or as an underslung load. The other major role is that of casualty or medical evacuation support, for which up to six stretchers can be fitted. The aircraft can operate in a wide variety of inhospitable conditions ranging from desert to arctic environments. The Puma also has a proud history of providing relief aid in humanitarian operations.

Powerplant
Two Turbomeca Turmo 3-C4 turbines
Thrust: 1300shp each

Dimensions
Length:	14.08m
Rotor:	15.09m
Height:	4.54m
Weight:	7.4 tonnes
AAR:	No
Speed:	147kts
Ceiling:	17,000ft
Aircrew:	2 pilots (or one pilot, one WSO), one WSOp

Weapon Systems
Missiles:	None
Bombs:	None
Guns:	Two 7.62mm GP machine guns

Sensors
None

Defensive Aids
Missile warning system (AAR-47)
Radar warning receiver
Infrared jammer (ALQ-144A)
Chaff and flare dispensers

> GRIFFIN HAR2

The Griffin HAR2 is used as a multirole helicopter by 84 Squadron at RAF Akrotiri, Cyprus. The Squadron operates four aircraft, supplied and maintained by the civilian company FBH services, but operated by experienced military aircrews. The HAR2 is used for Search and Rescue duties over land in mountainous terrain during the day and over the sea at night by using night-vision goggles and its FLIR/TV turret. In the Support Helicopter role, the Griffin HAR2 carries six (eight if operationally essential) fully equipped troops from the smallest and dustiest of sites. The Griffin is also used in its HT1 form by DHFS Shawbury.

Powerplant
Two P&W PT6T- 3D turboshafts
Thrust: 900shp each

Dimensions
Length: 17.11m
Rotor: 14.02m
Height: 3.48m
Weight: 5.4 tonnes
AAR: No
Speed: 140kts
Ceiling: 20,000ft
Aircrew: SAR - One pilot,
                   WSO/Winch
                   Operator,
                   Winchman
                   SH - One pilot,
                   one crewman day,
                   3-man crew night

Weapon Systems
None

Sensors
Radar: Weather radar
Targeting: None
Search Recce: Ultraforce FLIR
                   Turret

Defensive Aids
None

> GRIFFIN HT1

Griffin HT1s are used for Multi-engine Advanced Rotary Wing training at DHFS Shawbury and for basic Search and Rescue training at RAF Valley. There are eleven aircraft in service; eight are based at RAF Shawbury and three are based at RAF Valley. The Griffin HT1, which is a military twin-engined helicopter derived from the civilian Bell Textron 412EP helicopter, has a cruising speed of 120kts and an endurance of almost 3 hours, which makes it ideally suited for advanced helicopter training. The Griffin is also used in its HAR2 form by No 84 Squadron in Cyprus.

Powerplant
Two P&W PT6T-3D turboshafts
Thrust: 900shp each

Dimensions
Length: 17.11m
Rotor: 14.02m
Height: 3.48m
Weight: 5.4 tonnes
AAR: No
Speed: 140kts
Ceiling: 20,000ft
Aircrew: One pilot instructor, one student. One rear crew instructor, one student

Weapon Systems
None

Sensors
None

Defensive Aids
None

ROYAL
AIR FORCE

> SQUIRREL HT1

The Squirrel HT1 is an ideal platform to teach the rudiments of rotary-wing flying and is used for Single Engine Basic and Advanced Rotary Wing training at the Defence Helicopter Flying School, RAF Shawbury. The Squirrel HT1 is also used by the CFS (Helicopter) Squadron for instructor training, and by 670 AAC Squadron, based at Middle Wallop, for operational training.

Powerplant
Ariel 1D1 gas-turbine engine
Thrust: 625shp

Dimensions
Length: 12.94m
Rotor: 10.69m
Height: 3.21m
Weight: 2.1 tonnes
AAR: No
Speed: 155kts
Ceiling: 16,000ft
Aircrew: One pilot
instructor, one
student

Weapon Systems
None

Sensors
None

Defensive Aids
None

ROYAL
AIR FORCE

SEA KING HAR3/3A

The Westland Sea King HAR3/3A is used in the Search and Rescue (SAR) role. The aircraft are operated from six locations around the UK, with each location supporting two aircraft. There is also a detachment of two HAR3s providing SAR cover in the Falkland Islands. The standard SAR crew is made up of four members: two pilots, one of whom is the aircraft captain, a radar operator who acts as the winch operator at the rescue scene and a winchman, normally trained to paramedic standard, who will supply immediate first-aid and recovery services at the rescue site.

Powerplant
Two R-R Gnome H1400-1 turboshafts
Thrust: 1389shp each

Dimensions
Length: 22.15m
Rotor: 18.9m
Height: 5.13m
Weight: 9.7 tonnes
AAR: No
Speed: 125kts
Ceiling: 10,000ft
Aircrew: Two pilots, one
                 radar/winch
                 operator, one
                 winchman

Weapon Systems
None

Sensors
Radar: ARI 5955
Targeting: None
Search Recce: FLIR Systems
                 Q-STAR Multi-
                 Sensor System

Defensive Aids
None

> AGUSTA A109E

The Agusta A109E Power helicopter is operated by No 32 (The Royal) Squadron in the VIP Transport and Communication roles. It can be flown by a single pilot in all weather conditions, by day and night. The twin-engine design gives the pilot more flexibility when planning routes over built-up areas, as the aircraft can operate at limited weights on a single engine; therefore, even if power from one engine is lost the aircraft can maintain height to clear the built-up area. The twin-engine design also increases safety margins when flying in and out of confined landing sites.

Powerplant
Two P&W PW206C turboshafts
Thrust: 561shp each

Dimensions
Length: 13.07m
Rotor: 10.99m
Height: 3.56m
Weight: 3 tonnes
Internal Fuel: 660kgs
AAR: No
Speed: 168kts
Ceiling: 20,000 ft
Range: 350nmls
Aircrew: One pilot

Weapon Systems
None

Sensors
None

Defensive Aids
None

ROYAL
AIR FORCE

FLYING TRAINING

HAWK T1/1A

The Hawk T1 is used solely for fast-jet pilot advanced flying training, whilst the T1A is used for weapons and tactical training for both pilots and weapon systems officers. The T1A is also used extensively for operational support-flying and is capable of undertaking a number of war roles. In its weapons and tactical training role the Hawk is used to teach air combat, air-to-air firing, air-to-ground firing and low-flying techniques and operational procedures. The Hawk T1A is also used by the RAF Aerobatic team, the Red Arrows.

Powerplant

R-R Turbomeca Adour turbofan
Thrust: 5200lb

Dimensions

Length:	11.9m
Wingspan:	9.39m
Height:	3.99m
Weight:	5.7 tonnes
AAR:	No
Speed:	550kts
Ceiling:	48,000ft
Aircrew:	One pilot instructor, one student

Weapon Systems

Missiles:	AIM-9L
Bombs:	BL 755
Gun:	Aden 30mm

Sensors

None

Defensive Aids

None

ROYAL AIR FORCE

> HAWK 128

The next generation Hawk aircraft, the Hawk 128, will enter service in 2008 as a replacement for some of the current Hawk TMk1s. The Hawk 128 will introduce student pilots to the digital cockpit environment they will experience in front-line operational service and will provide a seamless transition between advanced flying training and operational conversion training onto fighter aircraft such as the Typhoon F2 and the Joint Combat Aircraft.

Powerplant
R-R Adour 951 turbofan
Thrust: 6500lb

Dimensions
Length: 12.43m
Wingspan: 9.94m
Height: 3.98m
Weight: 9.10 tonnes
AAR: No
Speed: 555kts
Ceiling: 48,000ft
Aircrew: One pilot
                 instructor, one
                 student

Weapon Systems
Missiles: AIM-9L
Bombs: BL 755
Gun: None

Sensors
FLIR
Weapon aiming systems

Defensive Aids
None

ROYAL
AIR FORCE

Squadrons   CFS Tucano Squadron   Tucano Air Navigation Squadron   72(R) Squadron   207(R) Squadron

TUCANO T1

The Tucano provides basic fast-jet flying training to RAF and RN student pilots, and basic WSO training to all potential RAF WSOs. Student pilots fly around 130 hours during their training course on the Tucano before progressing to the Hawk T1 aircraft at RAF Valley. The Tucano's two-seat tandem cockpit makes it an ideal lead-in to the Hawk. The aircraft handling is similar to that of a jet aircraft and it is fully aerobatic, thus providing an excellent workhorse for training fast-jet pilots in all aspects of military flying.

Powerplant
Garrett TPE331-12B turboprop
Thrust: 1150shp

Dimensions
Length:	9.86m
Wingspan:	11.28m
Height:	3.4m
Weight:	3 tonnes
AAR:	No
Speed:	300kts
Ceiling:	25,000ft
Aircrew:	One pilot instructor, one student

Weapon Systems
None

Sensors
None

Defensive Aids
None

ROYAL AIR FORCE

> GROB 115E TUTOR

The Grob 115E Tutor is used for elementary flying training by 3 Elementary Flying Training Squadrons, 14 University Air Squadrons and 12 Air Experience Flights throughout the UK. It is also used by the Central Flying School and for elementary WSO training at the RAF College Cranwell. All of the Tutors in RAF service are provided and supported by Vosper Thornycroft Aviation. The Tutor's primary flight instruments are on the right-hand side of the cockpit, thus allowing the student to fly the aircraft from the right-hand seat with a right-hand stick and a left-hand throttle so that future transition to fast-jet aircraft is made easier. The combination of docile handling characteristics and good performance make it very suitable for its training role.

Powerplant
Textron Lycoming AEIO-360 B1F
Rating: 180hp

Dimensions
Length: 7.54m
Wingspan: 10.0m
Height: 2.4m
Weight: 990kg
AAR: No
Speed: 135kts
Ceiling: 10,000ft
Aircrew: One pilot
                       instructor, one
                       student

Weapon Systems
None

Sensors
None

Defensive Aids
None

ROYAL AIR FORCE

> FIREFLY T67

The Firefly is used for training pilots who have completed elementary flying training and have been selected for multi-engine training on the King Air B200. The aircraft are civilian registered and are owned, supplied and maintained by Babcock Defence Services, who provide the aircraft under contract to the RAF. The Firefly can carry two pilots for over three hours of training. This endurance, coupled with a rapid climb rate of less than 10 minutes to reach 10,000ft, make it an excellent training aircraft.

Powerplant
Textron Lycoming flat six-cylinder
Rating: 260hp

Dimensions
Length: 7.54m
Wingspan: 10.72m
Height: 2.29m
Weight: 1.2 tonnes
AAR: No
Speed: 156kts
Ceiling: 10,000ft
Aircrew: One pilot
                       instructor, one
                       student

Weapon Systems
None

Sensors
None

Defensive Aids
None

> BEECH KING AIR B200

The Beech King Air B200 is used as an advanced, multi-engine pilot trainer. Students learn advanced skills such as formation flying, low-level flying and airways navigation, and are expected to plan and manage composite missions involving several aircraft. Multicrew skills are taught with the emphasis shifting in the advanced phase towards developing captaincy and crew resource management skills. The King Air B200 has proved popular with students and instructors alike and its combination of a well-proven airframe with advanced cockpit and systems make it an ideal training platform for the new generation of multi-engine aircraft entering RAF service.

Powerplant
Two P&W PT6A-42 turboprops
Rating: 850shp each

Dimensions
Length:	13.36m
Wingspan:	16.61m
Height:	4.52m
Weight:	5.7 tonnes
AAR:	No
Speed:	259kts
Ceiling:	28,000ft
Aircrew:	One pilot instructor, up to 2 students, up to 5 passengers.

Weapon Systems
None

Sensors
Radar:	Collins WXR-270 weather radar
Targeting:	None
Reconnaissance:	None

Defensive Aids
None

ROYAL
AIR FORCE

> DOMINIE T1

The Dominie T1 is used to train weapon systems officers and operators, air engineers and air loadmasters in systems management, air leadership, decision making and teamwork to meet the operational demands of the RAF. The aircraft has a maximum crew of six and is generally operated with one pilot captain, with the remaining aircrew comprising a balance of up to five students and instructors. Dominie tasks include a mix of low, medium and high-level training sorties, and trials flights conducted for the Air Warfare Centre at RAF Waddington.

Powerplant
Two R-R Viper Mk301 turbojets
Thrust: 3310lb each

Dimensions
Length: 14.48m
Wingspan: 14.33m
Height: 4.87m
Weight: 9.5 tonnes
AAR: No
Speed: 284kts
Ceiling: 42,000ft
Aircrew: One pilot,
                       5 students/
                       instructors

Weapon Systems
None

Sensors
Radar: Super Searcher
                       ground mapping
Targeting: None
Reconnaissance: None

Defensive Aids
None

ROYAL AIR FORCE

> GROB 109B VIGILANT T1

Grob 109B Vigilant motor gliders are used by the Air Cadet Organisation at 17 Volunteer Gliding Squadrons located at various sites around the UK to give basic flying and gliding training to air cadets. Their role is to train air cadets in basic flying techniques and to enable them to reach a standard where they are able to fly solo. The Vigilant is a cost-effective, modern aircraft and its docile handling characteristics, combined with good fuel economy, make it an excellent training aircraft for cadets and instructors alike.

Powerplant
Grob 2500E1 horizontally opposed
four-cylinder, air-cooled
Rating: 95hp

Dimensions
Length: 8.1m
Wingspan: 17.4m
Height: 1.7m
Weight: 908kg
AAR: No
Speed: 130kts
Ceiling: 8000ft
Aircrew: One pilot
instructor, one
student

Weapon Systems
None

Sensors
None

Defensive Aids
None

ROYAL AIR FORCE

Squadrons Volunteer Gliding Squadrons

> GROB G103A VIKING T1

Grob G103A Viking gliders are used by the Air Cadet Organisation to give basic gliding training to air cadets. The aircraft is currently used by 10 Volunteer Gliding Squadrons located at various sites around the UK. Their role is to train air cadets to a standard that will allow them to fly solo. The Viking is a high performance sailplane, which can be winch-launched or aero-towed, and is used for basic training, high-performance flying and simple aerobatic flying. It is a cost-effective, modern glider, ideally suited to its training role with the Air Cadet Organisation.

Powerplant
Winch launch or aero tow

Dimensions
Length:	8.18m
Wingspan:	17.5m
Height:	1.55m
Weight:	625kg
AAR:	No
Speed:	119kts
Ceiling:	8000ft
Aircrew:	One pilot instructor, one student

Weapon Systems
None

Sensors
None

Defensive Aids
None

ROYAL
AIR FORCE

WEAPONS OF THE RAF

AIR-TO-GROUND

AIR-TO-AIR

MARITIME

AIRCRAFT GUNS

RECONNAISSANCE

TARGETING

ROYAL
AIR FORCE

AIRCRAFT 2

WEAPONS 88

AIRCRAFT WEAPONS

ROYAL
AIR FORCE

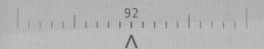

> ALARM

TORNADO GR4, TORNADO F3, TYPHOON F2

The Air Launched Anti-Radiation Missile (ALARM) is designed to destroy or suppress the use of enemy ground-based air-defence radar systems. ALARM operates by homing onto the radar energy being emitted by the target radar and can loiter in the area if the radar is switched off. It can also be pre-programmed to box-search for specific hostile radars after launch and then attack the highest priority threat.

Dimensions
Length:	4.3m
Diameter:	0.24m
Span:	0.72m
Weight:	260kg

Performance
Range:	Classified
Speed:	Supersonic
Sensor:	Passive radar homing

> BRIMSTONE

TORNADO GR4, HARRIER GR9, TYPHOON F2

Brimstone is an advanced, rocket propelled, radar-guided weapon and can seek and destroy armoured targets at long range. In indirect attack mode, weapons are launched when the targets and their position are not visible to the attacking aircraft, whereas in direct attack mode the pilot uses an onboard sighting system to select the target. The target can lie off the aircraft's track, thus the pilot does not need to manoeuvre to release the weapons.

Dimensions
Length:	1.8m
Width:	0.3m
Weight:	49kg

Performance
Range:	10 nmls+
Speed:	Supersonic
Sensor:	Millimetric wave radar

ROYAL AIR FORCE

MAVERICK

HARRIER GR7/GR9

Dimensions
Length:	2.59m
Diameter:	0.31m
Span:	0.71m
Weight:	286kg

Performance
Speed:	Mach 0.8
Range:	6nmls+
Seeker:	Imaging Infrared

Maverick is designed for close air support and defence suppression and can be used against armour, ships, transport and fuel-storage facilities. The G2 version, with which the RAF is equipped, has an Infrared seeker, which gives the weapon a true all weather, day or night, 'fire-and-forget' capability against armoured and mobile targets.

> CRV-7 ROCKETS

HARRIER GR7/GR9, JAGUAR GR3A

CRV-7 rockets are launched from 19-missile pods in a pre-programmed ripple and are used to attack lightly protected installations, ships or armoured forces from a range of up to 3 nautical miles. They can be fitted with a high-explosive warhead for unarmoured targets, or a kinetic energy penetrate, which contains no explosives, for attacks on armoured targets.

Dimensions
Length:	1.3m
Weight:	11kg

ROYAL AIR FORCE

> # GENERAL PURPOSE BOMBS

TORNADO GR4, JAGUAR GR3A, HARRIER GR7/GR9

Dimensions

Length:	2.18m or 2.48kg
Width:	0.33m or 0.42m
Weight:	312kg or 505kg

The 312kg and 505kg general purpose bombs use unitary blast warheads and can be dropped as unguided freefall bombs or fitted with a retarder unit, allowing aircraft to drop a bomb at low level over the target and get clear before detonation. Both bombs have three modes of detonation: above a target in airburst mode, impact detonation, or post-impact detonation after a pre-set delay.

> BL755 CLUSTER BOMB

HARRIER GR7, TORNADO GR4, JAGUAR GR3A

Dimensions

Length:	2.45m
Diameter:	0.41m
Weight:	277kg

When BL755 is released it breaks open in the airflow and releases 147 high-explosive bomblets into the target area, thus allowing multiple targets to be attacked with one weapon. The BL755 and upgraded IBL755 are used against vehicles and equipment and are delivered from low-level attacks. The RBL755 is a further upgrade which has an enhanced anti-armour capability and can be delivered from a medium-level attack, thus allowing the aircraft to operate from a safer altitude. The complete range of cluster bombs will shortly be withdrawn from RAF service.

ROYAL AIR FORCE

PAVEWAY II & PAVEWAY III

HARRIER GR7/GR9, TORNADO GR4, JAGUAR GR3A, TYPHOON F2

Paveway II is a precision laser-guided bomb which can be dropped from low or medium level and is homed onto its target by an airborne TIALD pod or from troops on the ground using a laser designator. The bomb's guidance package steers the bomb onto the source of reflected laser energy. Paveway III is a larger, upgraded LGB and is designed specifically to defeat hardened targets such as protected underground command posts. Paveway III equips Tornado GR4 aircraft.

Dimensions	
Length:	3.68m (PII)
	4.45m (PIII)
Width:	0.42m (PII)
	0.92m (PIII)
Weight:	546kg (PII)
	1141kg (PIII)

> ENHANCED PAVEWAY II & PAVEWAY III

HARRIER GR7/GR9, TORNADO GR4, TYPHOON F2

Dimensions

Length:	3.68m (EPWII)
	4.39m (EPWIII)
Width:	0.42m (EPWII)
	0.92m (EPWIII)
Weight:	545kg (EPWII)
	1130kg (EPWIII)

The Enhanced Paveway II and III laser-guided weapons give the RAF the ability to strike static, mobile and armoured targets accurately in all weathers and for 24-hours a day. Both EPWII and EPWIII are based on Paveway II and Paveway III respectively. Once released, EPW is fully autonomous in cases where there is cloud cover over the target which may obstruct the laser and prevent weapon guidance.

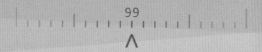

O ROYAL
AIR FORCE

> PAVEWAY IV

HARRIER GR9, TORNADO GR4, TYPHOON F2

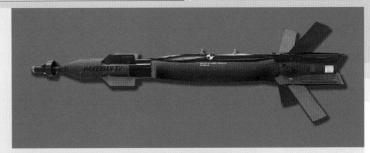

This advanced and highly accurate weapon will provide the RAF with a state-of-the-art precision guided bomb when it enters service in 2007 to replace the Paveway II weapons and the 505kg unguided general-purpose bombs. Equipped with the latest Global Positioning Guidance technology, Paveway IV is a low-cost, all-weather, 24-hour precision bomb capable of destroying the majority of general-purpose targets while significantly mimimising collateral damage. The first platform to receive the weapon will be the Harrier GR9 with Tornado GR4 and Typhoon F2 to follow.

Dimensions
Length:	3.1m
Width:	0.42m
Weight:	225kg

STORM SHADOW

TORNADO GR4, TYPHOON F2

Dimensions
Length: 5.1m
Wing span: 3m
Weight: 1.3 tonnes

Performance
Speed: Mach 0.8
Range: 130nmls+

Storm Shadow is a long-range, stand-off, air-launched missile and is arguably the most advanced weapon of its kind in the world. The missile is equipped with a powerful conventional warhead and is designed to attack important hardened targets such as buried and protected command centres. Mission and target data is loaded into the weapon's main computer before the aircraft leaves on its mission. After release, the wings deploy and the weapon navigates its way to the target at low level using terrain profile matching and an integrated Global Positioning System.

> AIM-9L SIDEWINDER

TORNADO F3/GR4, HARRIER GR7/GR9, JAGUAR GR3A, HAWK T1A

Sidewinder is a supersonic, heat-seeking, short range, air-to-air missile with a IR seeker that guides the missile to impact by homing on the engine exhaust of the target aircraft. IR homing allows the missile to be used by day or by night and in electronic countermeasure conditions. The Sidewinder is a fire-and-forget 'dogfight' missile, allowing the pilot to fire several missiles at different targets within a very short time frame.

Dimensions
Length: 2.87m
Diameter: 0.13m
Weight: 84kg

Performance
Range: 6nmls+
Speed: Mach 3+
Sensor: IR reticule
               seeker

SKYFLASH

TORNADO F3

Dimensions
Length:	3.66m
Diameter:	0.21m
Span:	1.02m
Weight:	208kg

Performance
Range:	20nmls+
Speed:	Mach 2
Sensor:	Inertial mid-course/Active radar terminal

Skyflash is a medium-range, all-weather, air-to-air missile able to engage targets at ultra-high or low level in a variety of countermeasure environments. The missile uses semi-active homing, where the launch aircraft illuminates the target and the missile uses its own radar receiver to home on the reflected energy. Although Skyflash is primarily a BVR missile, it can also be employed at shorter ranges to ensure quick reaction times and maximum manoeuvrability after it has been launched.

ROYAL
AIR FORCE

AIM-132 ASRAAM

TORNADO F3, TYPHOON F2

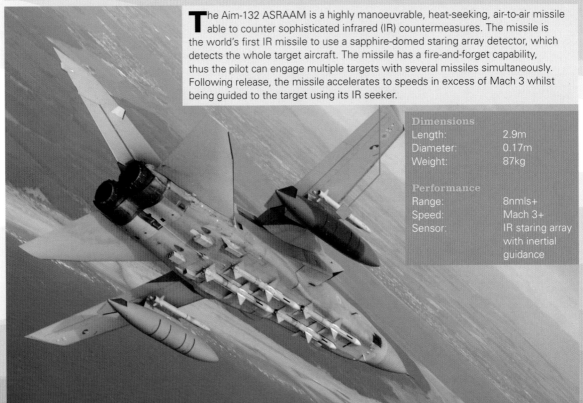

The Aim-132 ASRAAM is a highly manoeuvrable, heat-seeking, air-to-air missile able to counter sophisticated infrared (IR) countermeasures. The missile is the world's first IR missile to use a sapphire-domed staring array detector, which detects the whole target aircraft. The missile has a fire-and-forget capability, thus the pilot can engage multiple targets with several missiles simultaneously. Following release, the missile accelerates to speeds in excess of Mach 3 whilst being guided to the target using its IR seeker.

Dimensions
Length: 2.9m
Diameter: 0.17m
Weight: 87kg

Performance
Range: 8nmls+
Speed: Mach 3+
Sensor: IR staring array
            with inertial
            guidance

> AIM-120 AMRAAM

TORNADO F3, TYPHOON F2

Dimensions
Length:	3.66m
Diameter:	0.18m
Span:	0.53m
Weight:	157kg

Performance
Range:	20nmls+
Speed:	Mach 2.5+
Sensor:	Inertial mid-course/Active radar terminal

The AIM-120 AMRAAM incorporates an active radar with an inertial reference unit and a datalink microcomputer system. In a typical BVR engagement, the AMRAAM is launched from a range of 20nmls plus and is then guided by its own inertial navigation system, while receiving guidance updates from the launch aircraft via the data link. The missile's own monopulse radar then detects the target and guides it to impact.

> METEOR

TYPHOON F2

The Meteor missile is expected to enter service on RAF Typhoon aircraft early next decade. Meteor is designed around an airbreathing ramjet which boosts the weapon away from the launch aircraft and then remains under power until warhead detonation, giving the missile the energy to pursue and destroy the fastest and most agile aircraft at range. Its warhead carries impact and proximity fuses so targets can be destroyed even if the missile does not score a direct hit.

Dimensions
Length: 3.67m
Diameter: 0.18m
Weight: 185kg

Performance
Range:
Speed: Mach 4+
Sensor: Inertial mid-course/Active radar terminal

HARPOON

NIMROD MR2

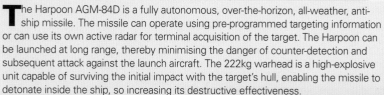

The Harpoon AGM-84D is a fully autonomous, over-the-horizon, all-weather, anti-ship missile. The missile can operate using pre-programmed targeting information or can use its own active radar for terminal acquisition of the target. The Harpoon can be launched at long range, thereby minimising the danger of counter-detection and subsequent attack against the launch aircraft. The 222kg warhead is a high-explosive unit capable of surviving the initial impact with the target's hull, enabling the missile to detonate inside the ship, so increasing its destructive effectiveness.

Powerplant
Integral turbojet motor

Dimensions
Length:	3.8m
Diameter:	0.35m
Weight:	527kg
Range:	68nmls
Warhead:	222kg
Guidance:	Inertial mid-course/ Terminal active radar
Target:	Surface shipping

ROYAL
AIR FORCE

> STING RAY

NIMROD MR2, NIMROD MRA4

Sting Ray is a lightweight, air-launched, electrically-powered, homing torpedo used against either deep ocean or coastal water submarines. The Sting Ray is an autonomous weapon which, having received pre-launch search pattern information from the launch aircraft, uses its active sonar and tactical software to search for, localise and attack its submarine target. Should the Sting Ray miss its target, it has the ability to turn and home in again for another attack.

Powerplant
Electric via sea water battery

Dimensions
Length:	2.6m
Diameter:	0.35m
Weight:	265kg
Max Depth:	Below 760m
Speed:	40+ knots
Guidance:	Pre-launch target information
Warhead:	29kg shaped charge
Target:	Submarines

> MAUSER CANNON

TORNADO F3, TORNADO GR4, TYPHOON F2

The Mauser 27mm cannon is a single-barrel, high performance, breech-cylinder gun operated by an electrically fired gas-operated system at a selective rate of 1000 or 1700 rounds per minute. Targeting of the cannon is done through the aircraft's head-up display by using either a prediction sight or, in the case of the F3, a radar designated sight. The cannon has a very high muzzle velocity and its high rate of fire, coupled with its ability to fire several different types of high-explosive shells, make it equally suitable for both interceptor-type aircraft and ground-attack aircraft alike.

ROYAL AIR FORCE

> ADEN CANNON

HAWK T1A, JAGUAR GR3A

The Aden 30mm cannon is a single-barrelled, five-chambered rotating cylinder gun, which is used by the Jaguar GR3A in the air-to-ground role and the Hawk T1A for air-to-air and air-to-ground training. It is electrically fired and gas operated with a rate of fire of between 1200 and 1400 rounds per minute. The Jaguar GR3A has two cannon housed in port and starboard gun bays in the lower centre fuselage, whilst the single cannon operated by the Hawk T1A is housed in an external gun-pod assembly bolted to the underside of the fuselage. The cannon can be harmonised with the aircraft's HUD to give a firing imagery display, which the pilot aligns onto the target.

M134 MINIGUN

CHINOOK HC2

The M134 Minigun is a 7.62mm air-cooled, percussion-fired, multi-barrelled rotary gun, which is mounted on the Chinook helicopter. The gun is electrically driven from the aircraft's 115V AC supply and is mounted on either the port or starboard side of the aircraft in the escape hatch or the cabin door respectively. The gun is fired manually, using belt-fed ammunition at up to 4000 rounds per minute.

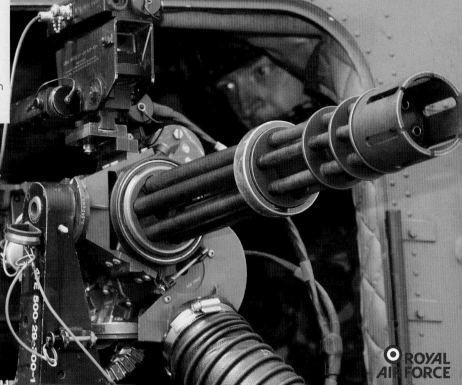

M60D MACHINE GUN

CHINOOK HC2

The M60D machine gun is a 7.62mm calibre gas operated machine gun that is mounted on the Chinook helicopter and can be fired from either side of the cabin, or from the aircraft's rear ramp. The gun is attached to a mount fixed to the aircraft that permits it to swivel freely between mechanical stops, which prevent damage to the aircraft during firing. The gun is fired manually at up to 550 rounds per minute.

> RAPTOR

TORNADO GR4

Reconnaissance Airborne Pod for Tornado, RAPTOR, is a stand-off electro-optical and Infrared long-range oblique-photography pod. The pod's high-resolution images can be transmitted via a real-time data-link to image analysts at a ground station, or can be displayed in the cockpit during flight. The RAPTOR system can create images of hundreds of separate targets in one sortie. The stand-off range of the sensors allows the aircraft to remain outside heavily-defended areas to minimise its exposure to enemy air-defence systems.

Dimensions

Length:	5.8m
Diameter:	0.8m
Height:	0.75m
Weight:	1000kg

ROYAL AIR FORCE

> DIGITAL JOINT RECONNAISSANCE POD

TORNADO GR4, HARRIER GR7/GR9, JAGUAR GR3A

The DJRP contains various electronically-scanned sensors, a number of electro-optical camera options and an Infrared Line Scanner. All sensors record to analogue tapes that provide high-resolution still or moving images of the target area to a software-based Ground Imagery Exploitation System. The enhanced digital capability of the pod could eventually enable it to send real-time, data-burst images to ISTAR aircraft for onward transmission direct to commanders on the battlefield.

Dimensions

Length:	2.81m
Diameter:	1.4m
Weight:	254kg

> PREDATOR A MQ1B

39 SQUADRON A FLIGHT (EMBEDDED WITHIN USAF)

Powerplant
One Rotax 914 4-cylinder piston
Thrust: 115 Hp

Dimensions
Length:	8.23m
Wingspan:	14.84m
Height:	17.34m
Weight:	1134kg
AAR:	No
Speed:	120 Kts
Ceiling:	25,000ft
Aircrew:	One pilot, one sensor operator

Weapon Systems
Missiles:	Hellfire AGM 114
Bombs:	None
Gun:	None

Sensors
Radar:	Lynx SAR (optional)
Targeting:	Multi-Spectral Targeting System (MTS-A)
Reconnaissance:	Video from MTS-A and SIGINT

Defensive Aids
None

The MQ1B Predator A is a medium-altitude, long-endurance, remotely piloted aircraft. Its primary role is to provide real-time reconnaissance video imagery to ground commanders, but it has the additional capability to strike against ground targets using Hellfire missiles. The basic operating crew is one pilot and a sensor operator who fly the Predator mission either locally from inside a portable Ground Control Station or via satellite links from Nellis AFB, Nevada.

ROYAL AIR FORCE

> PREDATOR B MQ9A

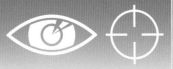

39 SQUADRON B FLIGHT (EMBEDDED WITHIN USAF)

The MQ9A Predator B Reaper is a high-altitude, long-endurance remotely piloted aircraft designed for surveillance, military reconnaissance and ground-attack missions. The aircraft is controlled by a pilot and sensor operator who are located in a Ground Control Station. Two cameras in the nose of the aircraft provide the pilot with a forward view using either daylight TV or Infrared, whilst the sensor operator controls the targeting pod. A KU band SATCOM system provides over the horizon control of the aircraft via a KU-band data link.

Powerplant
Honeywell TPE 331-10T turboprop
Thrust: 900SHP

Dimensions
Length:	10.97m
Wingspan:	20.12m
Height:	3.66m
Weight:	4763kg
AAR:	No
Speed:	250kts
Ceiling:	50,000ft
Aircrew:	One pilot, one sensor operator

Weapon Systems
Missiles:	Hellfire AGM 114
Bombs:	Paveway II or GBU JDAM
Gun:	None

Sensors
Radar:	Lynx SAR
Targeting:	Multi-Spectral Targeting System (MTS-A)
Reconnaissance:	Video from MTS-A and SIGINT

> TARANIS UAV

Project Taranis is a 4-year UAV technology demonstrator programme which will focus on the next generation of UAVs. Taranis will be about the size of a Hawk aircraft and will provide the MoD with experimental evidence on the potential capabilities of this class of UAV and help to inform decisions on the future mix of manned and unmanned fast-jet aircraft. UAVs will not replace any of the RAF's front line aircraft in the short term, but in the longer term a mix of manned and unmanned aircraft could be used on operations. Detailed Taranis designs will be unveiled early in 2008, while ground tests are expected to begin in 2009 with flight trials planned for 2010.

LITENING III

TORNADO GR4, TYPHOON F2

The Litening III laser targeting and reconnaissance pod provides a vital air-to-ground targeting capability, including the ability to laser-designate ground targets for attack by other assets, and a ground reconnaissance and scanning capability, even when the aircraft is flying at maximum speed at low altitudes and undertaking combat manoeuvres. The pod has additional operating modes including air-to-air targeting and is equipped with third-generation Forward Looking Infrared (FLIR) sensors, the images from which can be fed into the pilot's Head-Up Display to assist low-altitude supersonic night flying.

Dimensions

Length:	2.2m
Diameter:	40.6cm
Weight:	208kg

> TIALD

TORNADO GR4, HARRIER GR7/GR9, JAGUAR GR3A

TIALD (Thermal Imaging Airborne Laser Designator) is a second-generation laser designator pod which comprises a high-resolution FLIR, a laser designator and a tracking system. Once the pilot or WSO has identified the target on his cockpit display the aiming cross is positioned over the target and the pod is switched into automatic tracking mode. At the appropriate moment during the attack the TIALD laser is turned on, which provides the bomb's guidance system with the required information to complete the attack.

Dimensions

Length:	2.9m
Diameter:	0.3m
Weight:	230kg

ROYAL
AIR FORCE

RAF REGIMENT

ROYAL
AIR FORCE

> BROWNING 9MM

The Browning FN 9mm Self Loading Pistol is the issue side arm for the Royal Air Force and is used primarily as a self-protection weapon. It is a semi-automatic pistol that is chambered for the NATO standard 9mm x 19mm pistol round, also known as the 9mm luger and 9mm parabellum. The standard magazine holds 13 rounds.

> L85A2 INDIVIDUAL WEAPON

The L85A2 is the Heckler and Koch updated version of the SA80 L85 and is one of the most accurate individual weapons currently available. The weapon has been widely used on operations in a variety of demanding environments such as Sierra Leone, Afghanistan and Iraq.

Calibre:	5.56 mm
Length:	785 mm
Barrel Length:	518 mm
Weight:	4.98 kg
Muzzle Velocity:	940 m/s
Feed:	30 round magazine
Effective Range:	400m
Rate of Fire:	610-775 rpm

> L86A2 LIGHT SUPPORT WEAPON

The L86A2 Light Support Weapon is an extended-barrel version of the L85A2 and possesses extendable bi-pod legs, a rear grip and butt-strap that provide a more stable fire position, thus enabling higher volumes of fire and more effect at longer ranges.

Calibre:	5.56 mm
Length:	900 mm
Barrel Length:	646 mm
Weight:	6.58 kg
Muzzle Velocity:	970 m/s
Feed:	30 round magazine
Effective Range:	1000m
Rate of Fire:	610-775 rpm

> 40MM UNDER-SLUNG GRENADE LAUNCHER

The 40mm UGL is designed to be mounted beneath the barrel of the L85A2, and has been issued to each fire-team on RAF Regiment Field Squadrons. The UGL is able to fire 40mm High Explosive, smoke and illuminating rounds out to a range of 350m to destroy, obscure or indicate enemy positions.

ROYAL
AIR FORCE

> 5.56MM LIGHT MACHINE GUN

Calibre:	5.56mm
Length:	914mm
Barrel Length:	465mm
Weight:	7.1kg
Muzzle Velocity:	960m/s
Feed:	100-round disintegrating belt
Effective range:	800m
Rate of fire:	700-1000 rpm

The Minimi, or Light Machine Gun, is a belt-fed 5.56mm machine gun that is carried by RAF Regiment Squadron fire teams. It is a highly portable weapon system that can provide a high rate of fire because of the large amount of ammunition that can be carried. The LMG provides great utility and flexibility to RAF Regiment patrols.

> 7.62MM GENERAL PURPOSE MACHINE GUN

The GPMG is used as a Section Machine Gun, carried by a Gunner and fired using its bi-pod legs. It can also be used in the sustained fire role, grouped with other GPMGs and mounted on a tripod and fitted with the C2 optical sight. It is mainly used mounted on a Land Rover TUM in conjunction with the HMG.

Calibre:	7.62mm
Length:	1230mm
Barrel Length:	629mm
Weight:	13.85kg
Muzzle velocity:	838m/s
Feed:	100-round disintegrating belt
Effective range:	800m light role, 1800m sustained fire role
Rate of fire:	750 rpm

> 12.7MM HEAVY MACHINE GUN

The powerful L1A1 12.7mm HMG provides long-range and significant kinetic effect. Currently, the HMG provides integral close-range support from a ground mount tripod or fitted to a Land Rover TUM using a variety of sighting systems. The performance of the HMG has recently been enhanced with a new 'soft mount' (to limit recoil and improve accuracy) and a quick-change barrel.

Calibre:	12.7mm
Length:	1656mm
Barrel Length:	1143mm
Weight:	38.15kg
Muzzle Velocity:	915 m/s
Feed:	50-round disintegrating belt
Effective range:	2000m
Rate of fire:	485-635 rpm

ROYAL
AIR FORCE

> SNIPER RIFLES

Designed to achieve first-round hit at 600m and harassing fire out to 1100m, the superb Accuracy International L96 sniper rifle has been upgraded with a new x3 x12 x50 sight and spotting scope. Selected RAF Regiment units also use the L115A1 Long Range Rifle (LRR), which fires an 8.59mm bullet, heavier than the 7.62mm round of the L96, with a flatter trajectory and less likely to be deflected over extremely long ranges.

Sniper Rifle L96
Calibre:	7.62mm
Length:	1124-1194mm
Weight:	6.5kg
Muzzle Velocity:	838m/s
Feed:	10-round box
Effective range:	900m

Long Range Rifle L115A1
Calibre:	8.59mm
Length:	1300mm
Weight:	6.8kg
Muzzle Velocity:	936m/s
Feed:	5-round box
Effective range:	1100m

> 81MM MORTAR

The battle-proven L16A2 81mm Mortar delivers accurate High Explosive (HE), Smoke or Illuminating rounds out to a range of 5650m. The 81mm Mortar can be man-packed in three loads, but mortar detachments are normally vehicle-borne. The weapon system has undergone a mid-life upgrade which has included the addition of SPGR (Specialised Personal GPS Receiver) and LH40C (Laser), which combine to make the TLE (Target Locating Equipment). This generates a significant enhancement in first-round accuracy and the ease and speed with which accurate fire can be deployed.

Calibre:	81mm
Barrel length:	1280mm
Weight:	37.94kg
Muzzle Velocity:	225m/s
Max Range:	HE 5650m
Rate of Fire:	15 rounds per minute

> JAVELIN

Shortly due to be fielded with the RAF Regiment, Javelin is a shoulder-launched, man-portable, anti-armour weapon system, with a secondary target and surveillance capability. Its missile is a fire-and-forget missile, with lock-on before launch and automatic guide to the target. As the missile is soft launched, and is capable of being fired from within buildings or undercover, the weapon can engage armoured vehicles, bunkers, buildings and helicopters.

Launch Tube length:	1198mm
Weight:	11.8kg * (missile)
Weight:	6.4kg (Command Launch Unit)
Max Range:	2500m

ROYAL
AIR FORCE

Glossary

AAR	Air-to-Air Refuelling
ACSSU	Air Combat Service Support Unit
AEROMED	Aeromedical Evacuation
AESA	Advanced Electronically Scanned Array
AEW	Airborne Early Warning
ALARM	Air Launched Anti-Radiation Missile
AMRAAM	Advanced Medium Range Air-to-Air Missile
ASACS	Airborne Surveillance and Control System
ASRAAM	Advanced Short Range Air-to-Air Missile
ASTOR	Airborne Stand-Off Radar
ASW	Anti-Submarine Warfare
AT	Air Transport
AWACS	Airborne Warning & Control System
ARBS	Angle Rate Bombing System
BVR	Beyond Visual Range
CAP	Combat Air Patrol
CAS	Close Air Support
CASOM	Conventionally Armed Stand-Off Missile
DAS	Defensive Aids System
DHFS	Defence Helicopter Flying School
DIRCM	Directional Infrared Countermeasures
DJRP	Digital Joint Reconnaissance Pod
EAW	Expeditionary Air Wing
ECM	Electronic Countermeasures
EOTS	Electro-Optical Targeting System
ELINT	Electronic Intelligence
ESM	Electronic Support Measures
EW	Electronic Warfare
FLIR	Forward Looking Infrared
FOB	Forward Operating Base
GPMG	General Purpose Machine Gun
GPS	Global Positioning System
GR	Ground Attack Reconnaissance
HDU	Hose Drum Unit
HOTAS	Hands On Throttle and Stick
HUD	Head-Up Display
IFF	Identification Friend or Foe
IMINT	Imagery Intelligence
IMSAT	Imagery Satellite
INAS	Inertial Navigation and Attack System
IRCM	Infrared Countermeasures
ISTAR	Intelligence Surveillance Target Acquisition and Reconnaissance
JFH	Joint Force Harrier
JHC	Joint Helicopter Command
JRRF	Joint Rapid Reaction Force
JTIDS	Joint Tactical Information Distribution System
LAIRCM	Large Aircraft Infrared Countermeasures
LGB	Laser Guided Bomb
LMG	Light Machine Gun
LTM	Laser Target Marker
LRMTS	Laser Ranging and Marked Target Seeker
MAD	Magnetic Anomaly Detector
MAWS	Missile Approach Warning System
MR	Maritime Reconnaissance
MRA	Maritime Reconnaissance & Attack
NBC	Nuclear Biological Chemical
NVG	Night-vision Goggles
OAS	Offensive Air Support
OCA	Offensive Counter Air
PJHQ	Permanent Joint Headquarters
RAIDS	Rangeless Airborne Instrumentation and Debriefing System
RAPTOR	Reconnaissance Airborne Pod Tornado
RWR	Radar Warning Receiver
SAR	Synthetic Aperture Radar
SATCOM	Satellite Communications
SEAD	Suppression of Enemy Air Defences
SH	Support Helicopter
SIGINT	Signals Intelligence
STOVL	Short Take-Off Vertical Landing
TIALD	Thermal Imaging Airborne Laser Designator
TS	Transport Support
UAV	Unmanned Aerial Vehicle
WSO	Weapon Systems Officer
WSOp	Weapon Systems Operator